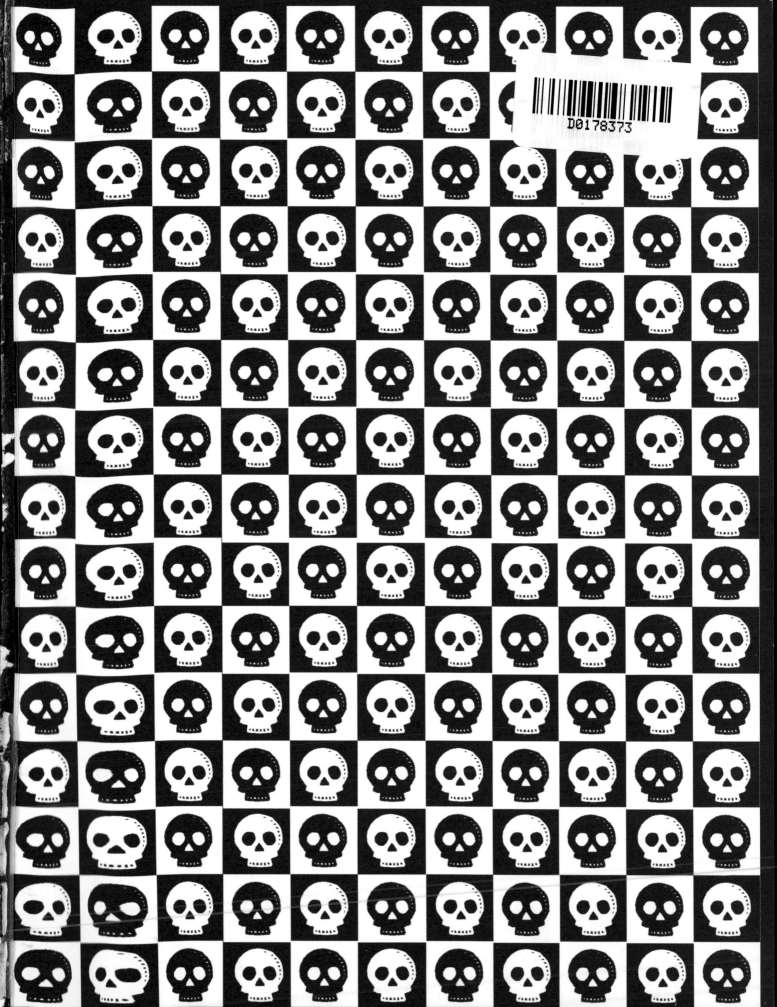

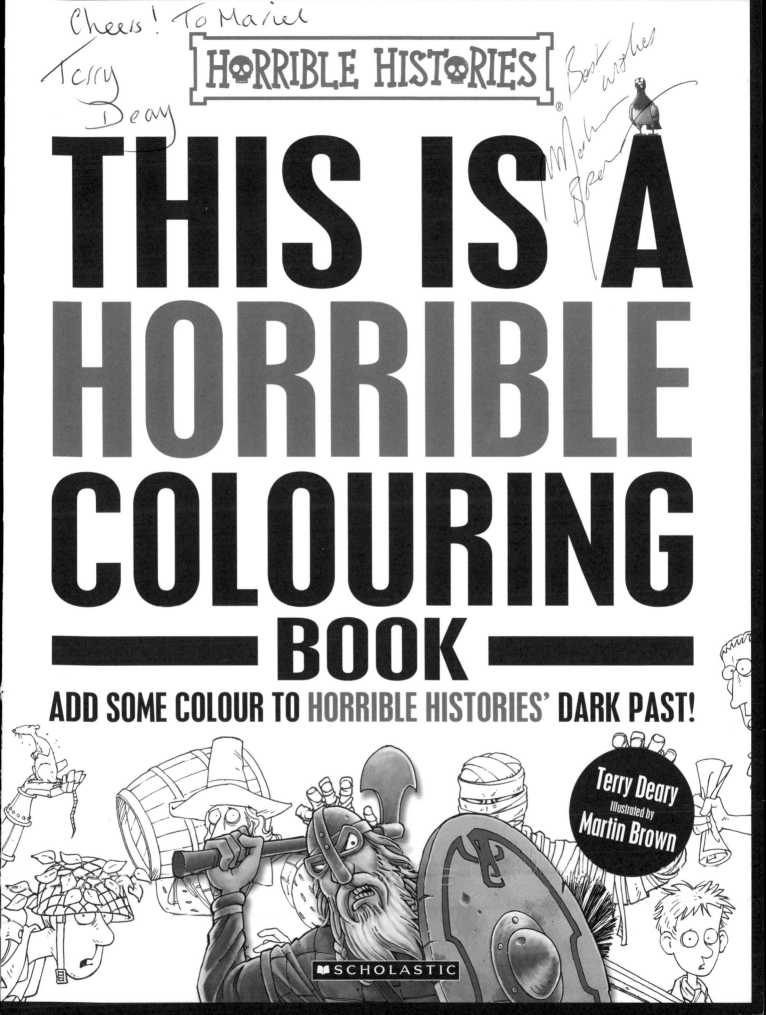

HORRIBLE HISTORIES

THIS IS A HORRIBLE COLOURING BOOK

ADD SOME COLOUR TO HORRIBLE HISTORIES' DARK PAST!

Terry Deary

Illustrated by Martin Brown

SCHOLASTIC

Scholastic Children's Books,
Euston House, 24 Eversholt Street,
London, NW1 1DB, UK

A division of Scholastic Ltd
London ~ New York ~ Toronto ~ Sydney ~ Auckland
Mexico City ~ New Delhi ~ Hong Kong

Published in the UK by Scholastic Ltd, 2017

ISBN 978 1407 17983 4

Printed in Malaysia

2 4 6 8 10 9 7 5 3 1

www.scholastic.co.uk

AWFUL EGYPTIANS

5500 BC–30 BC

AWESOME EGYPTIANS

The most awesome fact about the Egyptians was that their civilisation lasted an awfully long time — over 5,000 years. They had been around so long that their monuments were ancient even in Greek and Roman times.

STONEHENGE

They say sounds would bounce off the stones and they could act like giant amplifiers. Drums played in a Stone Age ceremony would boom around and sound as exciting as a modern pop concert.

FOUL FACT
The first brain surgeons lived in the New Stone Age. They were able to peel back the scalp with stone knives then drill holes in the skull with a sharp flint drill.

ADD SOME COLOUR TO THIS ANIMAL PRINT

I'VE GOT A MAMMOTH BRAIN!

3,500,000 YEARS AGO

Footprints have been found in East Africa that are over three-and-a-half million years old. They show that creatures we call 'hominids' could walk on two legs. Big deal, you say! Even a baby in nappies can do that! Yes, but this allows the front feet to develop into hands and to use tools. These 'hominids' will take over the world, you'll see.

DID YOU KNOW?

The nasty Neanderthals seem to have been head-hunters. Skulls have been found which show they were clubbed to death. The base of the skulls had been opened up to get the brains out... to eat?

SAVAGE STONE AGE

450,000 BC–2000 BC

People in the Stone Age used to paint on the walls of caves. Colouring pictures was invented long before writing. Long before even "Horrible Histories" were invented. Pictures of hunters killing animals – and sometimes a hunter being killed by an animal. Gory stories told in pictures.

What would happen today if you were to take a pot of paint and paint on the walls of your house or your school? Yes, you would be punished. Of course it won't hurt as much as the old punishments – children in schools were beaten with sticks or straps. The worst you will get today will be scraped knuckles from scrubbing off your artwork. It's no good moaning, 'I was only doing what humans were doing thousands of years ago.' Parents and teachers will want you to suffer.

But you love colouring pictures, don't you? 'So what is the answer?' you cry. I'm glad you asked. The answer is to colour in a BOOK. Drawing is hard. But what if you had a book of black-and-white pictures and you had to colour them in? Perfect. You can colour like a stone-ager and not make anyone angry.

Of course, like those cave-painters you want something gruesome to colour in. Pictures of horrible and gory things from the past.

'Where will I get a wonderful book like that?' you cry. (You do a lot of crying, don't you?)

'It's in your hands right now,' I cry back. 'What are you waiting for?'

'Extra red paint,' you say... with an evil laugh. Hurr! Hurr! Hurr!

MAD MUMMIES!

The ancient Egyptians believed that one day the world would end. When this happened, they thought that everyone who had a body would move on to a wonderful afterlife. But if your body rotted away, you couldn't live in the afterlife. The Egyptians felt it was their duty to make sure that their dead pharaohs didn't rot. So they turned them into mummies.

ASK YOUR MUMMY FOR HELP WITH THIS ONE

FOUL FACT
Herodotus, a Greek, visited Egypt in 455 BC and said, 'They first take an iron hook and draw out the brain through the nostril'.

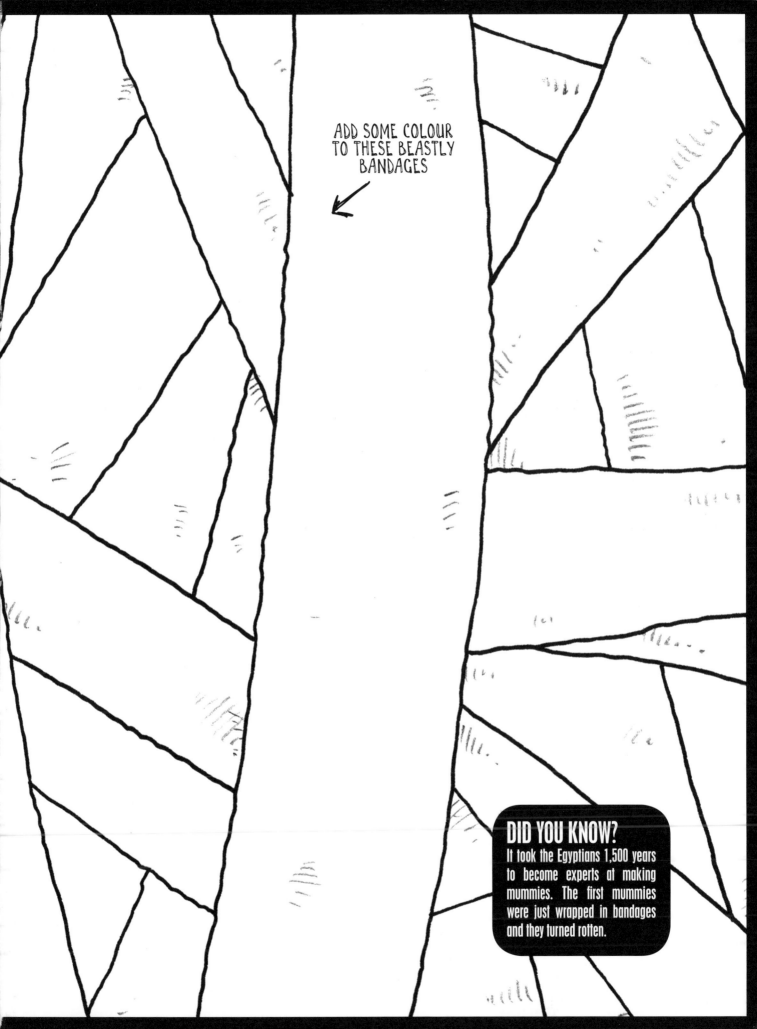

ADD SOME COLOUR TO THESE BEASTLY BANDAGES

DID YOU KNOW?
It took the Egyptians 1,500 years to become experts at making mummies. The first mummies were just wrapped in bandages and they turned rotten.

TUTANKHAMUN

Tutankhamun was a young pharaoh who became king at just nine years old. He reigned for ten years and died when he was 19. He's most famous for his tomb, which was discovered by a man named Howard Carter and his team in 1922.

The tomb of Tutankhamun was robbed twice shortly after his funeral.

HIEROGLYPHICS

The Egyptian writing is called hieroglyphics... but the Egyptians didn't call it that! The word is Greek — from *heiros* meaning *sacred* and *gluphe* meaning carving. The Egyptian name for it meant 'words of the Gods'.

Hieroglyphics were deliberately complicated so that it took a long time to read and write them. It meant that those who could read and write were more important.

MUMMY'S THE WORD!

PYRAMIDS

A pharaoh called Khufu ordered his builders to create the biggest pyramid of them all. It used over 2.3 million blocks of stone, and some of them weighed nearly 14 tonnes! Khufu's finished pyramid is called 'The Great Pyramid' and it's one of the Seven Wonders of the Ancient World.

CLEOPATRA
69 BC–30 BC

Cleopatra is probably the most famous Egyptian queen... except she wasn't an Egyptian queen. She ruled after Egypt was conquered by the Greeks. She was the seventh of that name and took the throne when she was about 17 years old.

The famous story is that Cleopatra killed herself, bitten by a venomous snake... an asp. It's tricky killing yourself that way. BUT... No one wrote about Cleo's death at the time it happened. The story of the asp was written a hundred years after she died. Maybe Cleo didn't kill herself — maybe she was murdered by her enemies.

CLEOPATRA, COMING AT YA!

GROOVY
GREEKS

1600 BC—AD 146

FOUL FACT

The Greeks fought against the Scythians. A Scythian soldier had a horrible custom. He would drink the blood of the first man he killed.

JULIUS CAESAR
100 BC–44 BC

Julius Caesar was one of the greatest Roman leaders. He was so successful he was murdered... by his friend! Rome had been run as a 'republic' for many years. That is to say the important people in Rome decided what to do. Then Julius Caesar became so powerful there was a fear that he'd take over. The people thought he wanted to become 'King of the Romans'.

HAVE A STAB AT COLOURING IN CAESAR

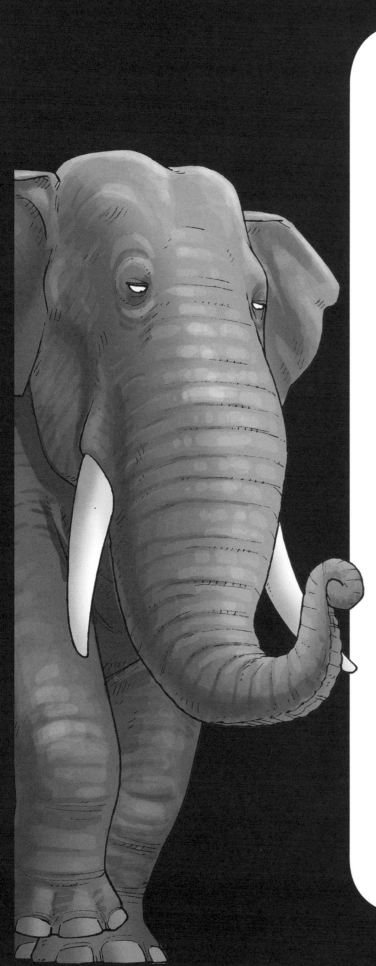

The Romans didn't just kill their enemies in massacres and battles. They killed them for SPORT. The mighty Colosseum took eight years to build and could hold 50,000 people – as big as a modern sports stadium. The Romans could watch gladiators, animal hunts and even sea battles. The opening of the Colosseum was to be the goriest games the world had ever seen.

In AD 107, after Emperor Trajan had won great battle victories in Dacia, he decided to have a party with Colosseum games killing 11,000 animals and 10,000 gladiators. Those games went on for 123 days. They ran out of animals to slaughter.

Over the next 300 years, half a million people and over a million wild animals died in the Colosseum 'games'.

TODAY'S EVENTS

MORNING
ANIMAL HUNTS

LUNCHTIME
EXECUTIONS

AFTERNOON
GLADIATORS

They would have seen... men against panthers, lions, leopards, tigers — but the men were usually heavily armed with spears, flaming torches, bows, lances and daggers. One spectator made a joke about the emperor, Domitian. He was taken out of the crowd and thrown to a pack of dogs!

WHO TURNED OUT THE LIGHTS?

ADD YOUR OWN DESIGN TO
THIS GLADIATOR'S SHIELD

THE ROTTEN ROMAN ARMY

In the early days of the Roman Republic, the Romans came up against the Greek king, Pyrrhus. The Greek strategy was to go into battle led by elephants. The elephants would charge at the Romans, trample them and send them running.

BAP!

IT'S THE ELEPHANT OF SURPRISE

But...

The clever Roman front line split in two. The elephants charged harmlessly through the line. They were too clumsy for the drivers to stop and turn. The helpless riders just kept going to the back of the Roman army, where there were special troops waiting with long, sharp spears. They jabbed the elephants until the maddened creatures turned round and charged back again. The elephants flattened the Greek army, who weren't expecting them!

CUT-THROAT CELTS

CELTS

750 BC–AD 520

BOUDICA
Died AD 61

Boudica is famous for revolting! The Romans robbed Boudica's Iceni tribe and flogged her. So in AD 61 she gathered an army and fought back. Her tribe attacked the Roman camps and murdered the men, women and children they found there.

Boudica didn't want to be a Roman slave so she took poison and died. Some say her body lies under Platform 8 of King's Cross Station in London.

ADD SOME LIFE TO THESE SAD SKULLS

The Celts believed that all life was made up of four 'elements' — air, earth, fire and water. They also believed that death could be explained by elements too! If there was a god of air then the Celts had to keep him or her happy by sacrificing someone using 'death by air' — suffocating, strangling or hanging. If there was a god of water then the sacrifice would be 'death by water' — drowning — and so on.

MEANWHILE, IN ITALY...
24 AUGUST AD 79

The citizens of Pompeii are minding their own business this hot summer's evening. Suddenly the nearby volcano, Vesuvius, erupts and smothers the town in choking, stinking, suffocating hot ash. Two thousand die but are preserved better than a fish finger at the North Pole. In 1748 archaeologists happily dig up the gruesome remains.

WHAT A BLAST!

SMASHING SAXONS

AD 410–1066

WICKED FOR WOMEN

In Saxon times divorce was rare... but there was another way to take a second wife while the first one was still alive. If your wife was carried away by an enemy you had to try to buy her back. But, if you couldn't afford to pay for her then you could take a new wife instead!

If a man was fed up with his first wife (and that has been known to happen) then he must have been tempted to go around making enemies. But there must have been a bit of girl power in Saxon times. If a man was captured by an enemy then a wife could take a new husband the same way.

ADD SOME MORE CLOUDS

YOO-HOO! MR VI-KING! MY HUSBAND'S OVER THERE!

ALFRED THE GREAT
871-899

King Alfred's famous for leading the fight against the Vikings. Alfred's armies forced the Vikings to make peace. He said, 'You Vikings keep the North and East — you can even call it Danelaw. My Saxons will keep the South and West. We'll call it Wessex.' And they had a deal. The Viking king of the Danelaw, Guthrum, even became a Christian like Alfred.

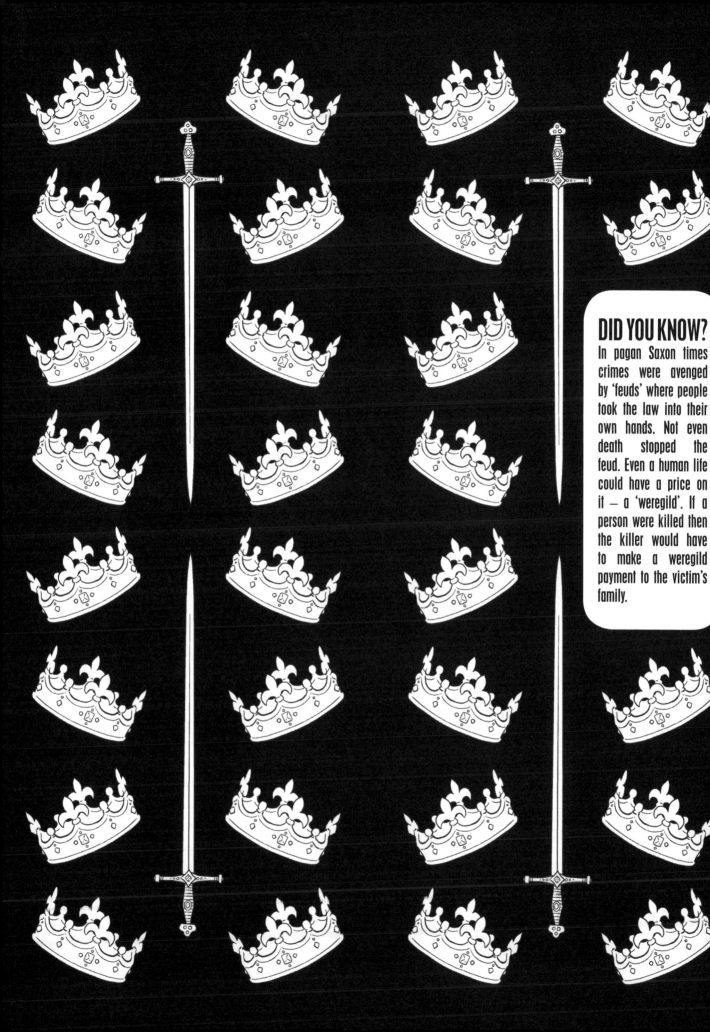

DID YOU KNOW?

In pagan Saxon times crimes were avenged by 'feuds' where people took the law into their own hands. Not even death stopped the feud. Even a human life could have a price on it – a 'weregild'. If a person were killed then the killer would have to make a weregild payment to the victim's family.

VICIOUS VIKINGS

787–1066

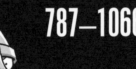

DID YOU KNOW?
No one was taken aboard a longboat unless they had proved they were skilled with an oar, a sword and an axe. The Vikings rarely took prisoners in sea battles because there was no room for them in the longboats. They let the losers drown or killed them.

FILL THE LONGBOATS WITH SOME CRUEL COLOUR

ARE WE THERE YET?
ARE WE THERE YET?
ARE WE THERE YET?
ARE WE THERE YET?

FOUL FACT
Vikings wore shoes of soft leather. But sometimes they left the fur of the animals on!

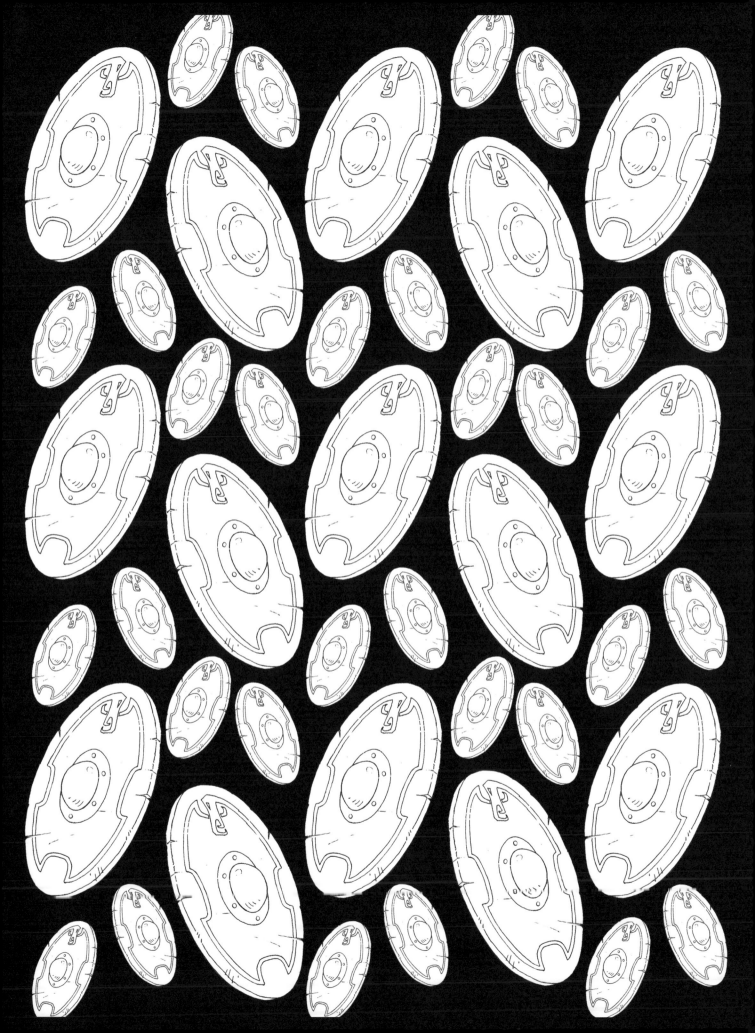

WANT TO KNOW WHY? WELL...

1. Easily netted and very tasty in Viking stew

2. Nothing wasted, goose feathers were also used for bedding and quilts

3. A great alternative to chicken and goose

4. Skins used for clothing

5. A wild version of today's pig

6. Meat was eaten and the fur made into clothes or used for trade with other countries

7. Waste not want not. Walrus ivory was in great demand from those in foreign countries

8. Roaming through massive forests by the fjords, even moose weren't safe from the Vikings' bows. Their antlers were used as knife handles and hair combs

9. The Vikings appear to have been the first whale hunters. It often took between 10 and 15 men to kill one whale, all taking turns to spear the poor creature. A long and painful death for the whale, but to the Vikings the whale was the scourge of the sea, often overturning ships, so it deserved to die

10. Even horses didn't escape the mighty Viking sword... yes, once the poor family nag was past it — chop!

STORMIN' NORMANS

1066–1300

WILLIAM I
1066-1087

William I was the first Norman king of England. Harold Godwinson of England was the heir to the Saxon throne when Edward the Confessor died (which he did in 1066). But in 1064 the story goes that Harold was crossing the English Channel when his ship was caught in a storm. Harold was recognised and taken to William of Normandy (who also fancied himself as King of England). Harold had to promise he would let William become king when old King Edward died. William set him free... and Harold broke his promise. That was William's excuse for invading England in 1066.

THE FEUDAL SYSTEM

William I became the last leader to conquer England when he won the Battle of Hastings. The Normans filled the country with castles. They also brought in the 'feudal system'.

This is the king who sits at the top and owns the lot.

These are the barons who guard the king's land, and train the men to fight for the king who sits at the top and owns the lot.

These are the knights who look after the villages, and fight for their barons who guard the king's land, and train the men to fight for the king who sits at the top and owns the lot.

These are the villeins and serfs who work on the land and work for the knights who look after the villages, who fight for their barons who guard the king's land, and train the men to fight for the king who sits at the top and owns the lot.

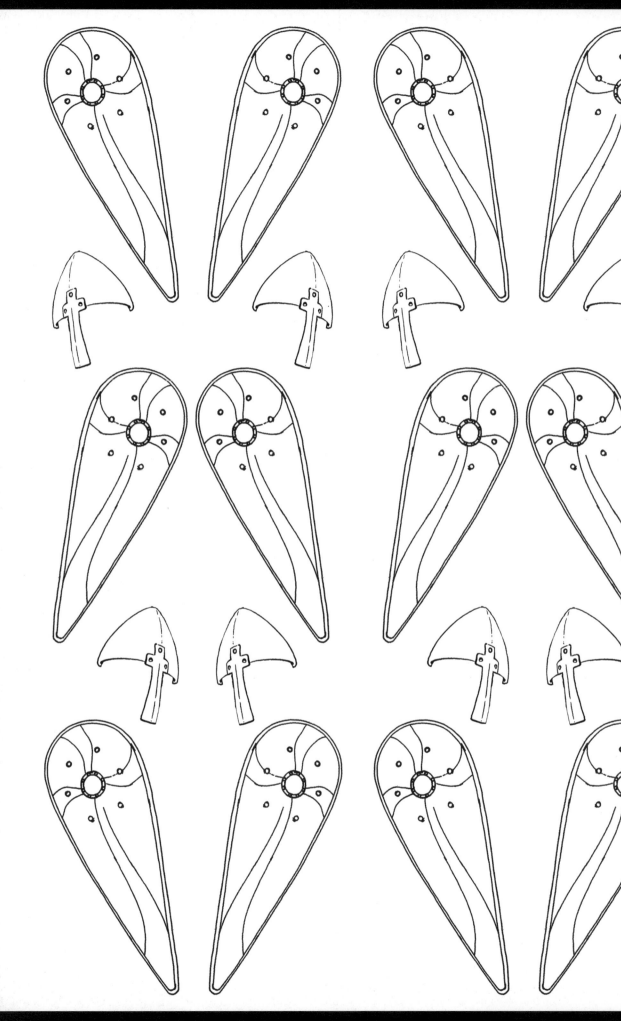

ADD MORE ARROWS

MERCENARY KNIGHTS

Many knights fought in the Crusades because they were Christians or because they were serving their lord. But some knights were 'mercenary' and fought because they were paid to fight. The punishment for a mercenary knight without a fight could be to have his armour taken away.

KING JOHN
1199–1216

King John was supposed to be the worst king England ever had. Legend says he wanted to steal the crown from Richard, and that he fought against Robin Hood to keep it. His angry barons made him sign a promise to give power to the people — this deed is known as the Magna Carta.

DID YOU KNOW?
From about the age of seven the sons of Norman lords and knights would train to be knights every afternoon. Good fun, eh? Riding and charging at targets (quintains) with your lance. Sword-fighting and murdering little rabbits and dear deer on hunting exhibitions.

ADD MORE ACTION THEN COLOUR IN

MEASLY MIDDLE AGES

1066—1492

DID YOU KNOW?

Historians usually start the Later Middle Ages at 1066 but history's been measly for much longer than that. In 410 the Romans in Britain went home. This is when the Early Middle Ages started — usually known as the Dark Ages.

ADD A DESIGN TO THIS NASTY KNIGHT'S SHIELD

FOUL FACT

In the measly Middle Ages peasants had a short life, but a miserable one. If overwork didn't kill you then you could die from ordinary things like a rotten tooth. Storing food over the winter could give you a type of food poisoning. Then there were the extra nice diseases to look forward to, like St Anthony's Fire – an arm or a leg would get a burning pain... then drop off. When you died you'd hope to go to heaven, but stories went that a peasant's soul didn't get to heaven – demons refused to carry it because of the horrible smell. They were really revolting!

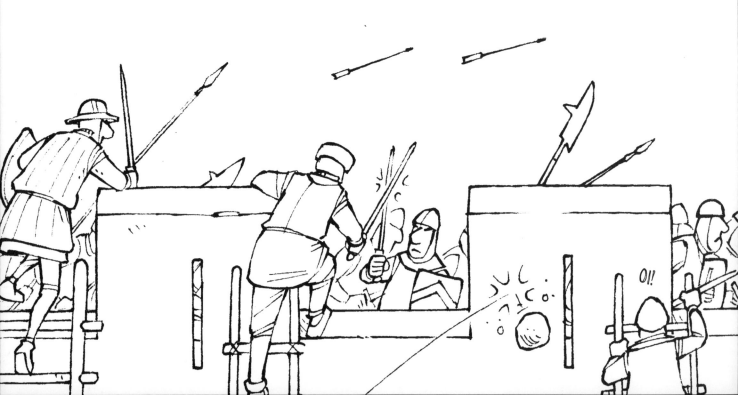

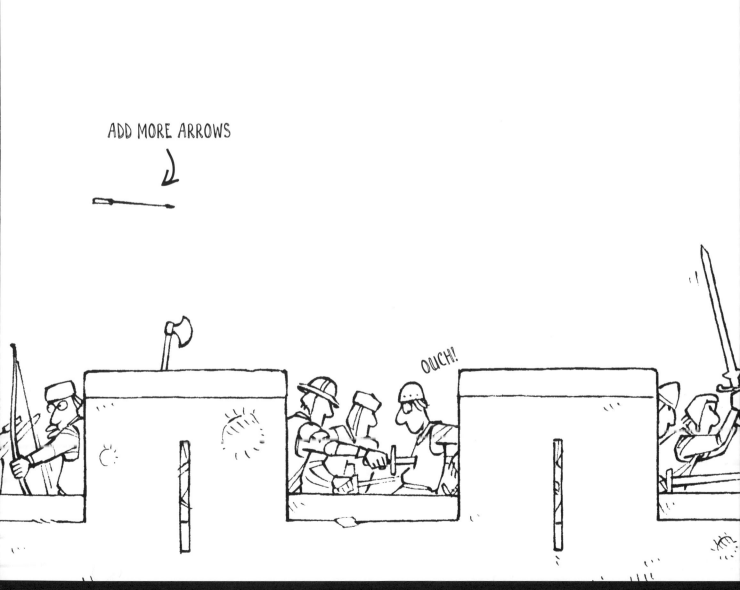

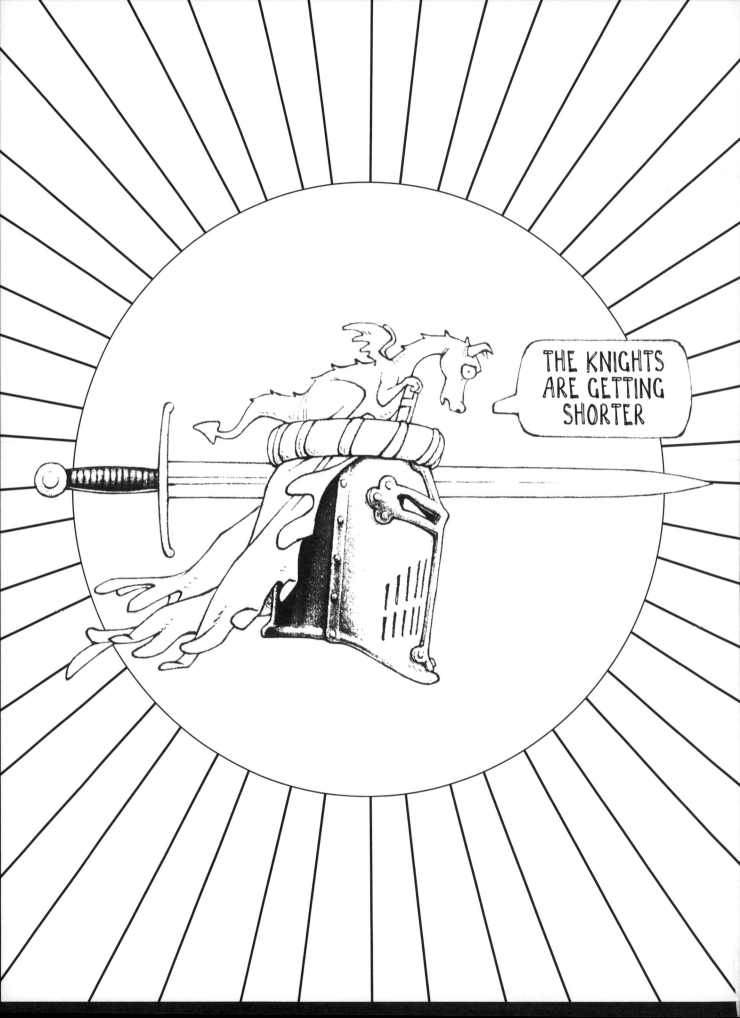

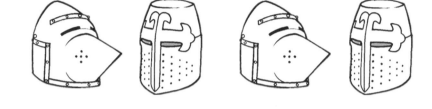

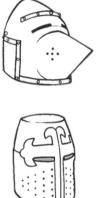
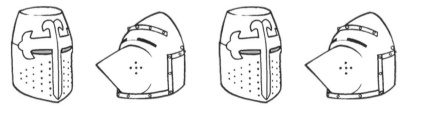

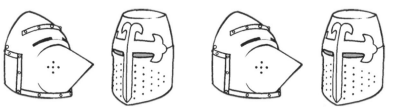

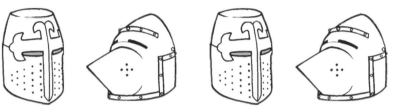

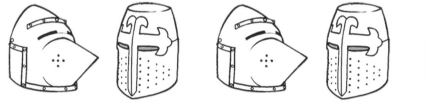

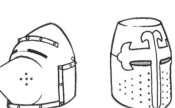

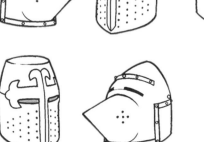

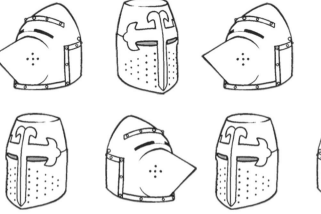

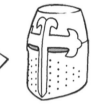
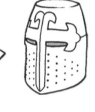
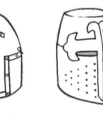

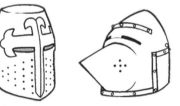

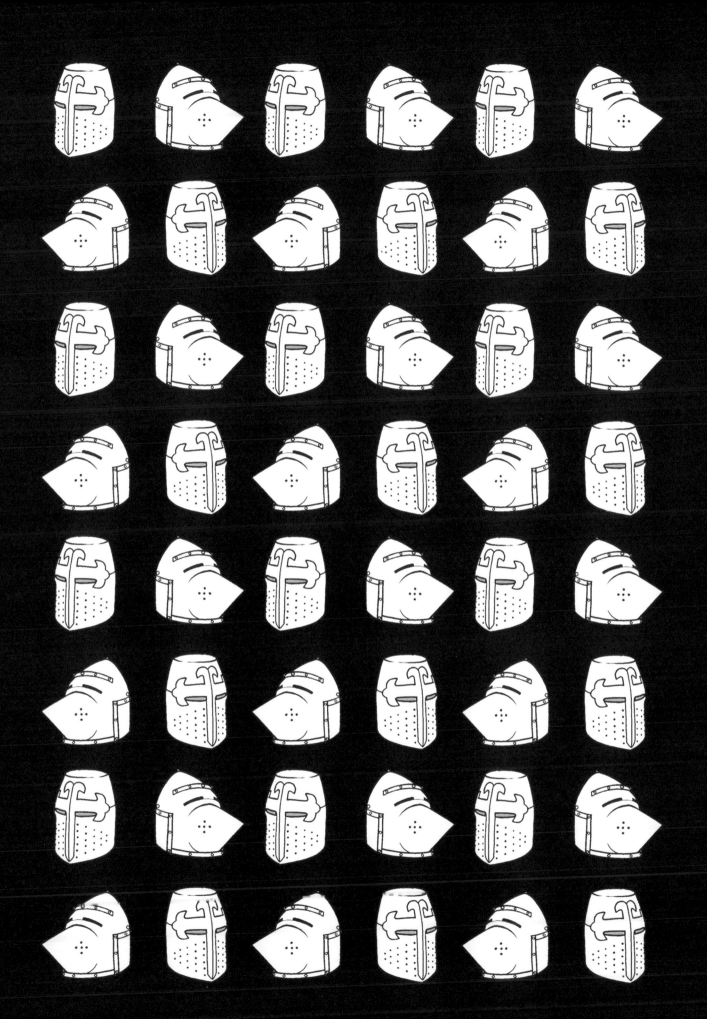

JOUST A MINUTE!

Tournaments started because knights wanted to fight and practise their skills. Early tournaments were usually known as 'mêlées'.

As well as mêlée tournaments there were jousts. A man in a can with a lance trying to knock another man in a can off his horse. Mêlées were for knights to practise their skills, but jousts were more for spectators.

DID YOU KNOW?
A knight could have an assistant, his squire, carry fresh weapons to him in the jousting area. But the squires sometimes got carried away and started using the weapons on the opposing squires. A new rule was invented. It said that any squire carrying a sword into the fighting area had to hold it by the point! Ouch!

DARK
KNIGHTS
and
DINGY
CASTLES

DID YOU KNOW?

If a knight wanted his son to grow up as a knight he would give the baby its first feed from the tip of his sword. (Don't try this at home with baby brothers!)

ROTTEN RANSOMS

Before the English fought the French in the Battle of Crécy in 1346, knights weren't often killed in battle... unless it was an accident. They were far too valuable alive. If you captured a knight then you could sell him back to his family for a fortune.

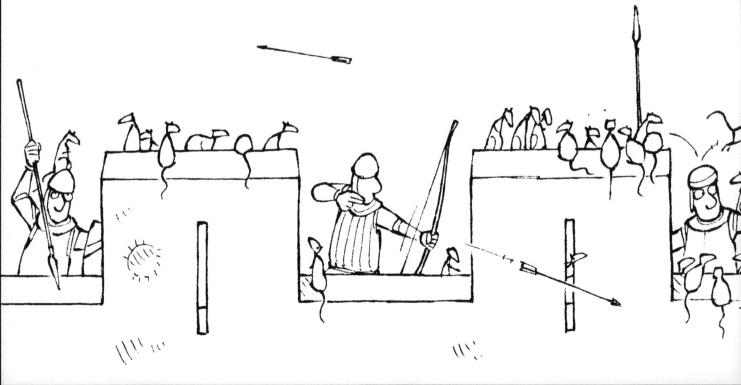

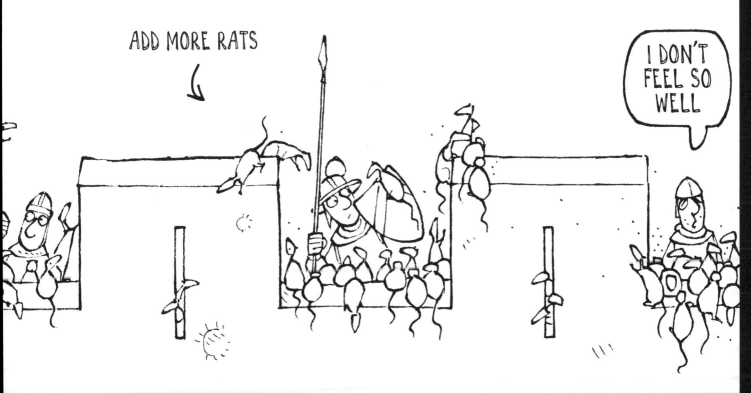

MEANWHILE, IN THE FAR EAST... 1214

Genghis Khan is the ruthless leader of the Mongol Empire. He had a nice motto you might like to follow: 'The defeated must die so the winners may be happy.' In other words, 'I'm not murdering you because I'm nasty – I'm doing it because it will make me happy.'

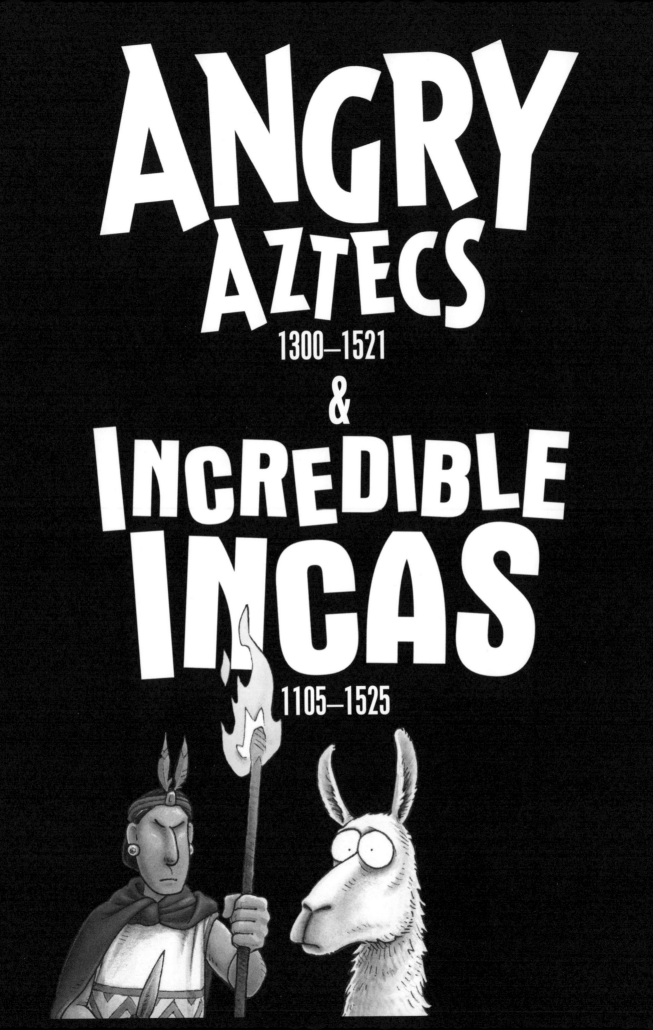

DID YOU KNOW?

If a family was very poor then there was a quick and easy way to make some money. Sell the kids! This was an idea the Aztecs copied from the Maya. Slave traders would buy healthy children and take them to market. The children would have to work hard for hours on end or be punished. A bit like school, really.

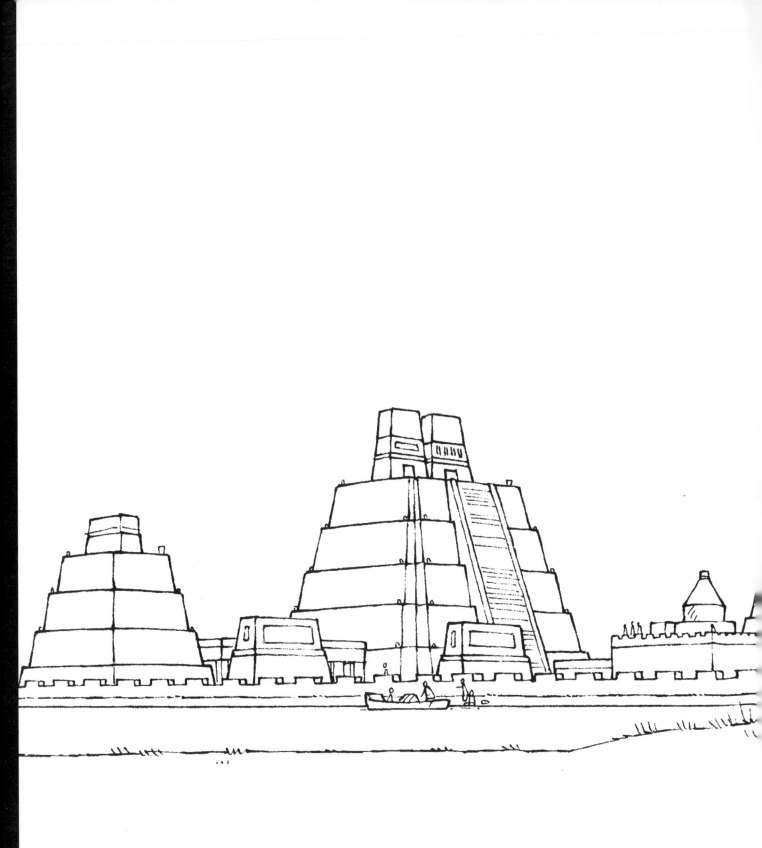

EVIL AZTECS

The Aztecs of Mexico were not very pleasant people. They attacked other tribes and sacrificed their prisoners to the gods. The victims were taken to the top of a pyramid and had their beating hearts ripped out with stone knives. The corpses were thrown down the side of the blood-soaked pyramid.

DON'T GET TOO CLOSE!

DID YOU KNOW?

The Aztecs said, 'If the gods had to give their hearts to keep the sun moving in the sky then we humans should do the same. We must make sure the sun is properly fed with regular supplies of heart.'

INCA STINKA

FOUL FACT

The Incas sacrificed all sorts to their sun god including llamas and even guinea pigs. But if the Incas were in desperate trouble – defeat in battle, famine or plague – only human blood was good enough to bribe the gods. And the purest blood was a child's blood. The Incas believed their gods preferred a nice sweet child!

RICHARD III
1452-1485

England was invaded by Henry Tudor. He landed in Wales and marched into England to meet Richard III in battle. Richard sat with his army on the top of Ambien Hill near Bosworth. As the battle turned against Richard's army, the king decided to charge down the hill and risk his own life. He was defeated.

Richard's body was stripped and dragged off to be buried in a forgotten grave in Leicester. In 2012 it was discovered again and dug up. It was found under a car park.

Henry Tudor brought a new and wonderful gift to the English people. Peace. The Red Rose Lancaster king married Elizabeth, daughter of White Rose York king Edward IV. The Wars of the Roses were finally over.

ADD SOME GOLD TO LIZ'S DRESS

HORRID HENRY
Henry VIII is famous for having six wives. He divorced two, beheaded two and one died. Fortunately for his last wife, Catherine Parr, she lived on after Henry died. As did his fourth wife, Anne of Cleves.

DID YOU KNOW?
In the space of just one year (1536) Henry's first wife (Catherine) died, his second (Anne Boleyn) was beheaded and he married his third (Jane Seymour).

WHAT IS A TERRIBLE TUDOR?

The Tudors were a family who ruled England, and poked their noses into the rest of Great Britain, from 1485 till 1603. The grandfather was Henry VII, his son was Henry VIII and the grandchildren were Edward VI, Mary I and Elizabeth I.

Five rulers and 118 years that changed the lives of the English people.

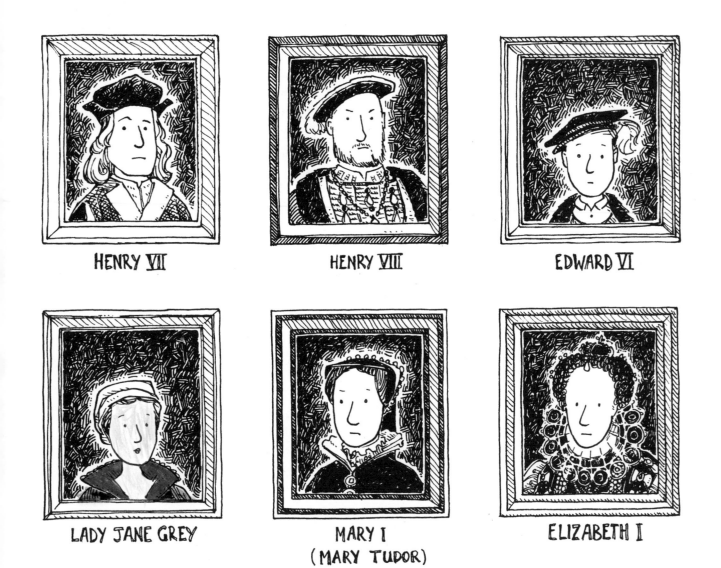

HENRY VII

HENRY VIII

EDWARD VI

LADY JANE GREY

MARY I
(MARY TUDOR)

ELIZABETH I

Henry VII's great-granddaughter, Lady Jane Grey, was put on the throne by Edward's Protector, and her father-in-law, the Duke of Northumberland. Lady Jane sat on the throne for only nine days before Mary Tudor raised an army and walloped Northumberland. So Lady Jane was pushed off her own throne and her head was pushed on the block.

MARY TUDOR
1516-1558

Henry VIII made England follow the Protestant religion. Mary took the throne and said everyone had to go back to being Catholic. The ones who refused were executed horribly. They were tied to a stake and burned. In a few years 300 English people were set alight, dying slowly and horribly. A writer gave her the name that stuck: Bloody Mary.

BLACK IS SO
LAST SEASON

THE TERRIBLE TUDORS

Tudor times were so bad that only one person in ten lived to the age of 40. Why? Because they were so filthy! Did you know? Open sewers ran through the streets, spreading diseases, and toilets were little more than a hole in the ground outside your back door.

THE SPANISH ARMADA
King Philip of Spain invades Queen Elizabeth's England in 1588. He wants his dead wife, Mary's, throne. He tries to invade with an armada of ships but the English navy nobbles him.

ARE WE THERE YET?
ARE WE THERE YET?
ARE WE THERE YET?
ARE WE THERE YET?

WICKED WORDS

SUPERSTAR SHAKESPEARE

William Shakespeare wrote poems and plays from about 1590 till 1616... then he stopped because he died and that made it a bit difficult.

BARMY
BRITISH EMPIRE

1562–1899

MEANWHILE, ALL ACROSS THE WORLD...
1580

Sir Francis Drake has sailed around the world and captured tons of Spanish gold. Britain will rule the seas for hundreds of years and take over dozens of countries — the British Empire.

CRUEL BRITANNIA

SLIMY STUARTS

1603—1714

1603
Queen Elizabeth dies and King James VI of Scotland becomes King James I of England. The first of the Slimy Stuarts.

DID YOU KNOW?
King James I was afraid of witches!

THE GUNPOWDER PLOT

In 1605 villains crept into the basement of the Houses of Parliament to blow it up but poor Guy Fawkes was caught.

Guy was caught at least 12 hours before Parliament was due to meet the king. And it wasn't 'luck'. The soldiers who caught Guy had been tipped off and were searching for explosives when they found him there. King James had also been tipped off. He was never in any real danger from the Gunpowder Plot.

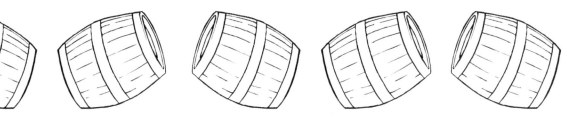

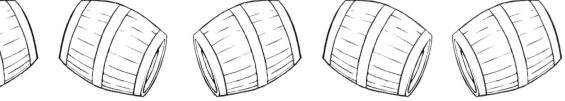

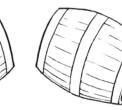

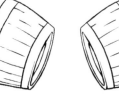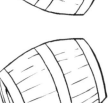

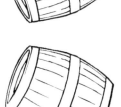

THE GREAT FIRE OF LONDON
1666

A little boy crept into Thomas Farriner's baker's shop in Pudding Lane. He reached up to steal a loaf that was cooling by the window. The baker swung round quickly. Too quickly — he scattered ashes over the wooden floor. The shop caught fire. Soon the whole street of wooden houses was burning fiercely. Burning sparks spread the fire to the next street, and the next. It seemed half of London was ablaze.

Witches

MEANWHILE, IN SALEM, USA...
1692

A group of girls aged nine to 12 start acting strangely. The doctor says it is because of witchcraft. This leads to a witch hunt where 19 women will be hanged. And the girls just made up the story.

BROOM, BROOM!

DID YOU KNOW?
The word 'witch' may have come from the old English word 'wicce' which means 'wise person'. Other people say it is from the word 'wik' which means twisted. All we need to know is it now means a person who meddles in magic. And witches have been around for a long, long time.

GORGEOUS GEORGIANS

1714–1830

HAIR TODAY,
GONE TOMORROW!

1714
The German Georges take the throne. Many Scots want the Slimy Stuart James III to be king so they rebel. These 'Jacobites' are defeated... and again in 1745.

1825

The first passenger train is driven from Darlington to Stockton. The end of the stagecoach age and the start of the railway age.

SORRY FOR THE HOLD UP

HORRID HIGHWAYMEN

Dick Turpin was a butcher boy until he decided there was more money in stealing cattle than chopping them. He joined 'The Essex Gang' of violent housebreakers. They entered someone's home, robbed it and tortured the occupants till they handed over their money and valuables.

WANTED

[ ]

Draw a picture of yourself here

NAME: _____

ALIAS: _____

WANTED FOR: _____

MOST HORRIBLE HABIT: _____

REWARD: _____

PERILOUS PIRATES

GORGEOUS GEORGIAN PIRATES

Have you ever seen a film about pirates? They were funny old characters, and liked a good laugh and a bottle of rum. They battled bravely against huge Spanish galleons and made the cowardly captains cough up some terrific treasure. Right? Wrong.

The terrible truth about the gorgeous Georgian pirates is that by Georgian times there were no Francis Drake characters attacking Spanish galleons and winning gold for England and the queen. They attacked little trading ships to steal tobacco or slaves or just spare sails and anchor cable. ('Your anchor cable or your life?' doesn't sound so gorgeous, does it?)

OI!

ADD SOME SMOKE TO
BLACKBEARD'S BEARD

BLACKBEARD
1680-1718

Blackbeard was a pirate you would NOT want to see at sea or cross cutlasses with in a cabin. He sometimes killed his own crew for sport and wore plaits in his hair so it looked like snakes were crawling over his face and head. He even twisted smoking rope into these plaits to add to his terrifying looks!

WHERE DID HE GO?

WICKED WEAPONS

Caribbean pirates used flintlock pistols, but they weren't all that deadly. They were noisy and they made clouds of smoke but were not very accurate. They took a long time to load and often didn't fire at all. Pirates like Blackbeard carried a dozen of them stuffed into his belt to save time. One of them would work sooner or later — or you could always throw them at your enemy.

DID YOU KNOW?

Pirates carried parrots. The parrots were captured in South America and carried back home. But they weren't just cute pets — they could be sold for good money in Europe. Pretty Polly made a pretty penny.

VILE VICTORIANS

1837—1901

QUEEN VICTORIA
1819-1901

Victoria ruled while the British Empire grew. She was made Empress of India and reigned over one quarter of all the people in the world. For all the riches this brought to Britain, many people in her home country lived terrible lives in slums.

And being Empress of India didn't make Queen Vic happy either. Her husband, Albert, died and she spent the rest of her life feeling sorry for herself. Albert was dead, but Victoria still made her servants lay out clean clothes for him every morning. It was as if he were alive and going to wake up and get dressed. This went on for 40 years.

GOD SAVE OUR GRACIOUS ME

FOUL FACT

In the early 1800s, children as young as five worked in the mines and were given a job as 'trapper'. A trapper's job was to sit by the doors in the tunnels and open them every time a coal truck came along. You were paid a penny a day – but if you bought a candle then it cost a half-penny a day... so most trappers sat in the dark.

ADD SOME SMOKE TO THE CHIMNEYS

MAKE THESE BOOKS LOOK OLD AND ADD A FEW WORDS OF YOUR OWN

CHARLES DICKENS
1812-1870

Charles Dickens was a very popular writer in Victorian times – even though he said some very nasty things about the Victorians! He was very much against hanging people in public, for example. Dickens said the crowds who gathered to see a hanging were as disgusting as the criminal who was being hanged. With the help of Dickens's writing the hideous spectacle was ended in the 1860s. That's the power of the word in the hands of a good writer.

BRIGHTEN UP THIS
VICTORIAN STREET SCENE

20TH CENTURY

1900–2000

THE NINETEEN-HUNDREDS

In 1900 Queen Victoria is on the throne. She rules over the British Empire — 400 million people, almost a quarter of all the world's inhabitants. This makes the people of Britain rather proud, you understand. The English think they are the best of the Brits and some of them can be unbearable. Sir Claude Champion de Crespigny is typical. He says, 'Where there is a daring deed to be done in any part of the world, an Englishman should leap to the front to accomplish it.' In the next 100 years a lot of Brits will die believing that.

YOU'LL NEED A LOT OF
WHITE FOR THIS PAGE

1912
Brit Captain Robert Scott and his team of four reached the South Pole on 17 January... but found Roald Amundsen from Norway had beaten them by five weeks. Scott wrote, 'It is a terrible disappointment... it will be a wearisome return.' It was worse than wearisome! It was dead wearisome. In fact they ended up wearisomely dead.

FRIGHTFUL
FIRST WORLD
WAR

1914–1918

1914

No one is surprised when a war breaks out in August 1914. Germany smashed France in the Franco-Prussian War of 1871 and it was just a matter of time before France tried to take its revenge. But people are surprised that the war is still going on by the end of 1914. The two sides are like two heavyweight boxers jumping into the ring. Each one expects a quick knockout. But they will end up slugging it out, toe to toe, till they are exhausted.

DID YOU KNOW?
In the trenches the soldiers found 'chatting' was a peaceful way to pass the quiet times. But 'chatting' didn't mean talking. It meant getting rid of 'chats' or lice from the seams of their tunics.

TRENCH FOOT

TRENCH TAIL

MESSAGE ROCKET

If you're in the trenches and want to send a message you don't want to be cycling or running through gunfire. Send a message in a rocket.

The rocket has fins you can twist. They can send the rocket 800 to 2,000 metres in the air. Try not to hit the general.

TERRIBLE TANKS

Tanks were also known as... land creepers, land ships, boojums, wibble-wobbles and whippets. Oddest of all, the first tank was called 'Little Willie' so some soldiers called their tanks 'Willies'.

MEANWHILE, IN AMERICA...
1929

In the 1920s alcohol was banned in the USA. That meant big money for the gangs who sold illegal booze. Al Capone was America's most famous gangster in Chicago. But Capone had to protect his money with some pretty violent men. And it didn't pay to upset Al. One man who tried to steal Capone's business was 'Bugs' Moran. Al Capone set up a very special Valentine's Day gift for 'Bugs', then Al went on holiday to Florida.

On 14 February 1929 Al Capone's gang dressed up as police and raided Bugs's hideout. As Bugs's gang put their hands in the air and threw down their guns, the fake cops machine-gunned them to death. It was known as 'The St Valentine's Day Massacre'.

WOEFUL

SECOND WORLD WAR

1939–1945

TANKS A LOT!

DID YOU KNOW?

During the war there were 'gas detectors' placed at street corners. These were supposed to light up if gas was in the air. They were never used. There was never ever a gas bomb attack on Britain... yet some people reckon gas masks were one of the great successes of the war! Why? Because Adolf Hitler knew about the gas masks. He knew it would be a waste of time to bomb people with gas when the people were so well prepared – so he didn't bother!

WARTIME WEAPONS

In wartime the side with the best weapons has an advantage. Potty profs and brainy boffins raced to create new ways of battering buildings, chewing up children, walloping women, splattering soldiers and pulverising pensioners.

The Brits invented Pykrete – a mixture of sawdust and water that was frozen to make a material tougher than concrete. Ships built of Pykrete would be unsinkable and win the war. The war ended before they could be built. Sounds daft – but it's terribly true.

ADD SOME COLOUR TO CAMOUFLAGE THESE HELMETS

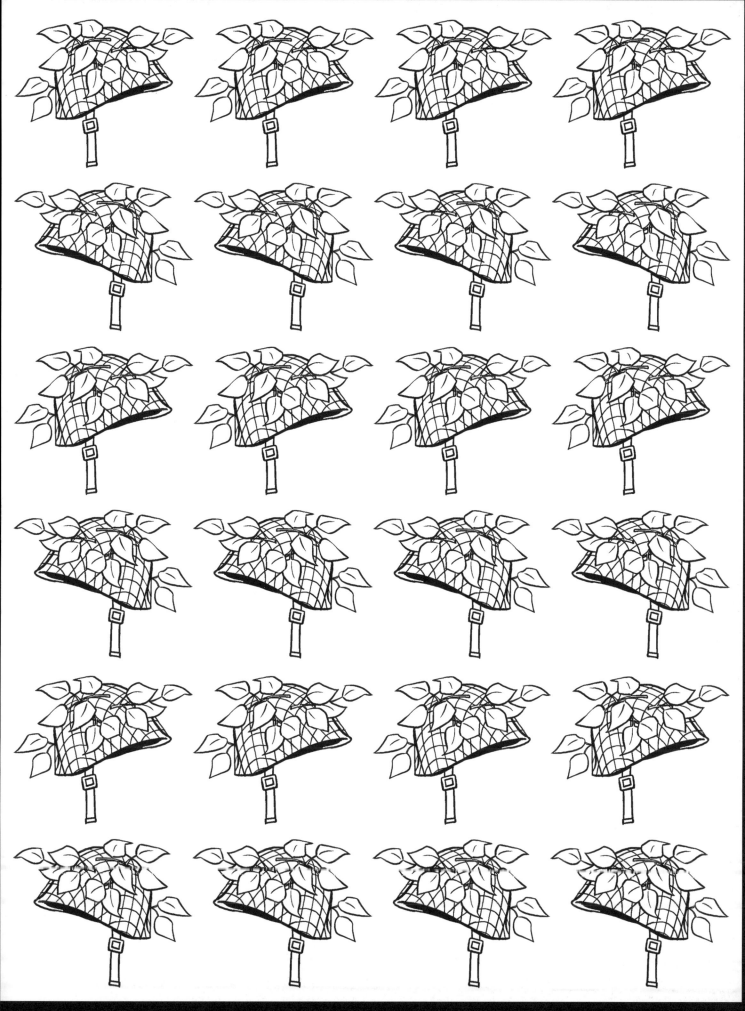

BLITZED BRITS

THE BLITZ
IS THE PITS

A WOEFUL WAR

The Second World War was different to past wars because you weren't safe anywhere. Innocent young people could be lying in bed reading a comic or studying at school or sitting on the toilet one moment – and be dead the next.

Bombs could blast you, saboteurs could spifflicate you and missiles marmalize you wherever you were. A battle area was known as a 'Front'. Now countries outside the war zones had their own 'Home Fronts'.

Horrible history happened at home as well as on battle fields.

DID YOU KNOW?

Some schools held gas mask tests. The children were sent to an air-raid shelter which was then filled with nasty (but not deadly) 'tear gas'. One class survived quite well except for poor little Charlie Bower. He found out the hard way that his mask had a leak — and spent the morning with tears streaming down his face!

In July 1940 Britain formed the Special Operations Executive — the SOE — to make secret war on its enemies. They trained the spies and invented secret weapons.

ROASTING RATS

Rats were everywhere. German workers would find dead ones in factories and throw them on the furnaces. So the cunning SOE made exploding rats. They shoved a stick of explosive up a dead rat's bum. Spies dropped the rats in the factory coal. The rats exploded inside the boilers and wrecked them. Soon German workers were scared to throw dead rats on the fire... even real, harmless dead rats... so the dead rats lay there and spread disease.

DID YOU KNOW?
Many spies in the Second World War were given small poison pills. If they were captured then they could crush the pill between their teeth, swallow the poison and die. This would save them from being tortured and betraying their friends.

ADD SOME COLOUR TO
RATTY'S DISGUISE

DISGUSTING DISGUISES

Most people think of false beards and wigs as quick disguises for spies. Cheek pads inside the mouth could change the shape of the face and some spies had surgery to alter their appearance.

DID YOU KNOW?

Agents usually dropped into France on parachutes. At first they used parachutes called 'A' parachutes, but these caused a lot of accidents. Splat! They switched to 'X' parachutes, which were packed in a different way and were safer.

NICE OF YOU
TO DROP IN

LATER, IN THE USA...
1969

The Americans landed on the moon. They announced it was not made of green cheese and flew home. Egyptian radio called it 'the greatest human achievement ever'. (The builders of their pyramids probably disagreed.)

I hope you had fun reading the foul facts and putting colour into those pictures. They were drawn by the brilliant Martin Brown. Your next step is to start making your own pictures. Start by copying Martin's maybe? There are dozens of "Horrible Histories" books for you to read and enjoy. One day you may become a great artist, rich and famous. When you do, don't forget to write 'Thank you, Terry Deary', on the back of a million-pound note and send it to me.

Yes, I will give marvellous Martin Brown a fair share – probably £13.57p. So get drawing!

Best of luck

Terry Deary

NOW YOU ARE A PRO, WHY NOT HAVE A GO AT COLOURING IN THE WHOLE WORLD?

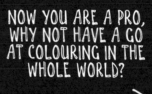

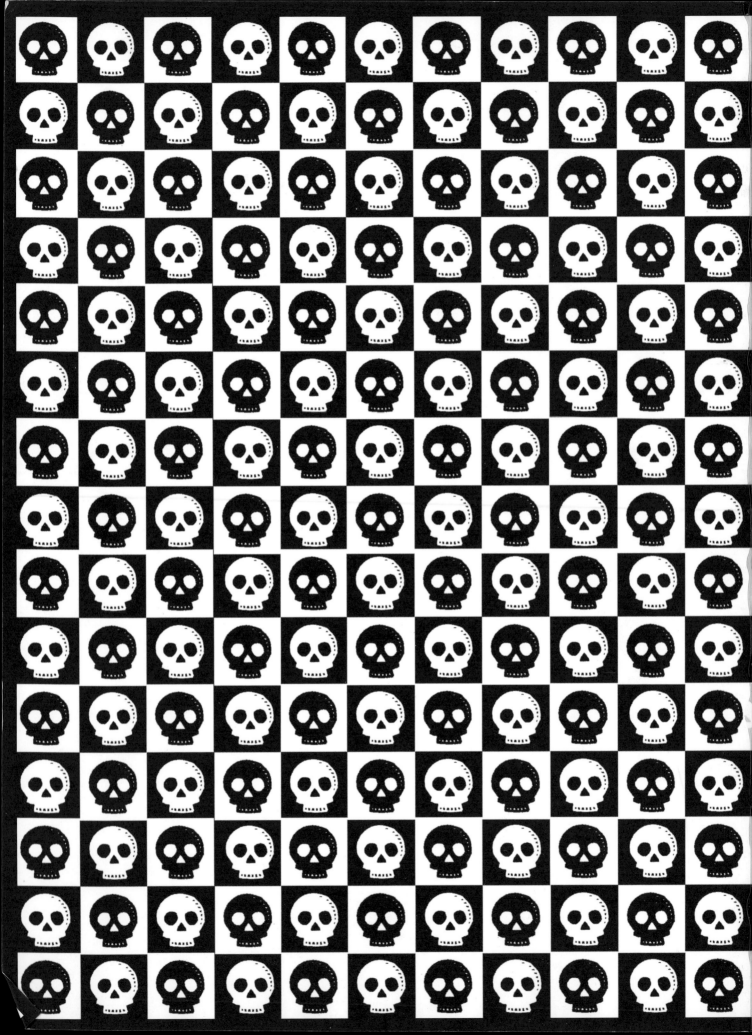